Andrew Brodie Basics

LET'S DO MENTAL MATHS

with over 100 reward stickers

FOR AGES 6-7

- Over 800 practice questions
- Regular progress tests
- Extra tips and brain booster questions

Andrew Brodie
An imprint of Bloomsbury Publishing Plc

50 Bedford Square
London
WC1B 3DP
UK

1385 Broadway
New York
NY 10018
USA

www.bloomsbury.com

ANDREW BRODIE is a trademark of Bloomsbury Publishing Plc

First published in Great Britain 2013

Copyright © Andrew Brodie, 2013

Cover and inside illustrations of Andrew Brodie and Digit the Dog © Nikalas Catlow, 2013

Andrew Brodie has asserted his right under the Copyright, Designs and Patents Act, 1988, to be identified as Author of this work.

A catalogue record for this book is available from the British Library.

ISBN
PB: 978 1 4081 8333 5

6 8 10 9 7

Designed and typeset by Marcus Duck Design
Printed and bound in China by Leo Paper Products

This book is produced using paper that is made from wood grown in managed, sustainable forests. It is natural, renewable and recyclable. The logging and manufacturing processes conform to the environmental regulations of the country of origin.

To find out more about our authors and books visit www.bloomsbury.com. Here you will find extracts, author interviews, details of forthcoming events and the option to sign up for our newsletters.

BLOOMSBURY

Notes for parents

What's in this book

This is the second book in an exciting new series of *Andrew Brodie Basics: Let's Do Mental Maths* books. Each book contains more than 800 mental maths questions specially devised to boost children's confidence by providing plenty of practice in all the key aspects of the National Curriculum:

• Number and place value
• Addition and subtraction
• Multiplication and division
• Fractions
• Measures
• Geometry

The structure of each test follows the same pattern but the questions become gradually more difficult as the book progresses. You will notice that some questions are repeated to help your child learn and then revise vital facts such as identifying shapes: squares, triangles, rectangles and circles. Taking the time to discuss the questions with your child and helping to explain anything they find difficult will produce the best results. Answers to all the questions are provided at the back of the book.

How you can help

To begin with your child might find the tests quite tricky but as they work their way through the book and become more familiar with the different types of question their confidence will grow. At the end of every five tests there is a Progress Test which will help you and your child to review some of the key concepts and will also highlight anything they haven't understood so far. Always provide lots of encouragement and explain that they should learn from their mistakes rather than be disheartened.

Children gain confidence by learning facts that they can use in their work at school. Help your child by displaying posters on their bedroom wall, showing facts such as the times tables, days of the week and months of the year. Talk about these facts with your child and other topics that children find difficult such as fractions.

Explain that the circle is cut into four pieces so we are dealing with quarters; 1 of these is shaded so the fraction shaded is one quarter. We write one quarter like this:

$$\frac{1}{4}$$

Digit the Dog and Brain Boosters

Look out for useful tips from Digit the Dog who provides little snippets of mathematical information that your child needs to know or quick questions to get them thinking!

Brodie's Brain Boosters feature short mathematical problems, which can be solved by working logically. Some of these may look very straightforward but the thinking processes that your child will need to apply are important skills to practise, ready for more challenging work later. Understanding the wording of questions is a crucial aspect of problem solving so ensure that your child reads each question carefully – give some help with the vocabulary if necessary.

With lots of practice and encouragement your child will see their score improve day by day!

TEST 1

1 What is the sum of 9 and 8?

2 6 + 7 =

3 12 + 8 =

4 What is the difference between 12 and 8?

5 9 – 5 =

6 11 – ___ = 5

7 6 x 5 =

8 9 x 2 =

9 7 x 10 =

10 30 ÷ 5 =

11 16 ÷ 2 =

12 80 ÷ 10 =

13 Count in ones: 68, 69, 70, 71… What number comes next?

14 Count in twos: 0, 2, 4, 6… What number comes next?

Brodie's Brain Booster

How many days are there in a fortnight?

15 What fraction is shaded?

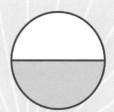

16 What time does the clock show?

17 How much money altogether?

18 What do the pears weigh?

19 How much liquid in the jug?

20 What shape is this?

3

Score:

1 What is the sum of 7 and 6?

2 9 + 5 =

3 13 + 7 =

4 What is the difference between 9 and 4?

5 7 − 3 =

6 13 −   = 8

7 3 x 5 =

8 7 x 2 =

9 6 x 10 =

10 40 ÷ 5 =

11 18 ÷ 2 =

12 90 ÷ 10 =

13 Count in ones: 85, 86, 87, 88…
What number comes next?

14 Count in twos: 14, 16, 18, 20…
What number comes next?

15 What fraction is shaded?

16 What time does the clock show?

17 How much money altogether?

18 What do the apples weigh?

19 How much liquid in the jug?

20 What shape is this?

Digit says...
Did you know that there are 24 hours in every day?

TEST 3

Score:

Brodie's Brain Booster

I have a 10p coin. How many 5p coins could I swap it for?

1 What is the sum of 8 and 6?

2 7 + 7 =

3 14 + 5 =

4 What is the difference between 15 and 8?

5 8 – 2 =

6 14 – ___ = 6

7 9 x 5 =

8 2 x 2 =

9 8 x 10 =

10 45 ÷ 5 =

11 22 ÷ 2 =

12 40 ÷ 10 =

13 Count in ones: 56, 57, 58, 59… What number comes next?

14 Count in twos: 24, 26, 28, 30… What number comes next?

15 What fraction is shaded?

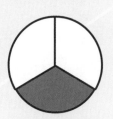

16 What time does the clock show?

17 How much money altogether?

18 What do the bananas weigh?

19 How much liquid in the jug?

20 What shape is this?

TEST 4

1 What is the sum of 6 and 7?

2 9 + 2 =

3 16 + 5 =

4 What is the difference between 17 and 9?

5 11 – 6 =

6 15 – ___ = 7

7 10 x 5 =

8 3 x 2 =

9 1 x 10 =

10 25 ÷ 5 =

11 10 ÷ 2 =

12 30 ÷ 10 =

13 Count in ones: 42, 43, 44, 45…
What number comes next?

14 Count in twos: 28, 30, 32, 34…
What number comes next?

15 What fraction is shaded?

16 What time does the clock show?

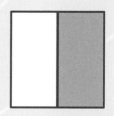

17 How much money altogether?

18 What do the oranges weigh?

19 How much liquid in the jug?

20 What shape is this?

Digit says…

Remember to say am for morning times. I get up at 7am for a nice bowl of dog food!

TEST 5

1 What is the sum of 7 and 4?

2 5 + 8 =

3 17 + 6 =

4 What is the difference between 13 and 8?

5 10 − 4 =

6 15 −   = 9

7 0 x 5 =

8 12 x 2 =

9 3 x 10 =

10 20 ÷ 5 =

11 12 ÷ 2 =

12 50 ÷ 10 =

13 Count in ones: 79, 80, 81, 82…
What number comes next?

14 Count in twos: 16, 18, 20, 22…
What number comes next?

15 What fraction is shaded?

16 What time does the clock show?

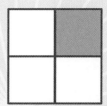

17 How much money altogether?

18 What do the figs weigh?

19 How much liquid in the jug?

20 What shape is this?

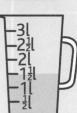

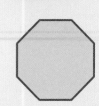

Addition

1 What is the sum of 8 and 7?

2 $8 + 8 =$

3 $19 + 5 =$

Subtraction

4 What is the difference between 13 and 7?

5 $10 - 6 =$

6 $14 - \boxed{} = 6$

Multiplication

7 $7 \times 5 =$

8 $0 \times 2 =$

9 $9 \times 10 =$

Division

10 $35 \div 5 =$

11 $14 \div 2 =$

12 $60 \div 10 =$

Number and place value

13 Count in ones: 75, 76, 77, 78…
What number comes next?

14 Count in twos: 34, 36, 38, 40…
What number comes next?

Fractions

15 What fraction is shaded?

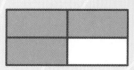

Measures

16 What time does the clock show?

17 How much money altogether?

16 What do the grapes weigh?

19 How much liquid in the jug?

Geometry

20 What shape is this?

Score chart

Test	1	2	3	4	5	Progress
Score						

8

TEST 6

1 Add 9 to 4.

2 8 + 6 =

3 13 + 7 =

4 12 subtract 7 =

5 12 – 4 =

6 10 – ⬚ = 6

7 7 x 5 =

8 Double 4 =

9 10 x 6 =

10 40 ÷ 5 =

11 Half of 18 =

12 100 ÷ 10 =

13 Count down in ones: 58, 57, 56, 55…
What number comes next?

14 Count in threes: 0, 3, 6, 9…
What number comes next?

15 What fraction is shaded?

16 What time does the clock show?

17 How much money altogether?

18 What do the mangoes weigh?

19 How much liquid in the jug?

20 What shape is this?

Digit says...

Remember to say pm for afternoon and evening times. I have some yummy dog biscuits for tea at 5pm!

9

TEST 7

1 Add 8 to 6.

2 9 + 7 =

3 12 + 9 =

4 14 subtract 6 =

5 16 – 8 =

6 10 – _____ = 4

7 3 x 5 =

8 Double 8 =

9 10 x 9 =

10 55 ÷ 5 =

11 Half of 20 =

12 60 ÷ 10 =

13 Count down in ones: 81, 80, 79, 78…
What number comes next?

14 Count in threes: 3, 6, 9, 12…
What number comes next?

15 What fraction is shaded?

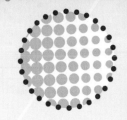

16 What time does the clock show?

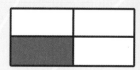

17 How much money altogether?

18 What does the pineapple weigh?

19 How much liquid in the jug?

20 What shape is this?

Brodie's Brain Booster

I have a 20p coin. How many 10p coins could I swap it for?

1 Add 7 to 5.

2 5 + 9 =

3 17 + 8 =

4 14 subtract 9 =

5 17 – 6 =

6 10 – ⬚ = 8

7 4 x 5 =

8 Double 6 =

9 10 x 2 =

10 15 ÷ 5 =

11 Half of 16 =

12 40 ÷ 10 =

13 Count down in ones: 85, 84, 83, 82…
What number comes next?

14 Count in threes: 15, 18, 21, 24…
What number comes next?

Digit says...

Did you know that there are 100p in a pound? Hmm, I wonder how many dog treats I could buy with that...

15 What fraction is shaded?

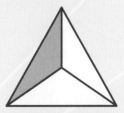

16 What time does the clock show?

17 How much money altogether?

18 What do the plums weigh?

19 How much liquid in the jug?

20 What shape is this?

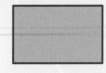

TEST 9

1. Add 8 to 5.

2. 6 + 7 =

3. 18 + 9 =

4. 13 subtract 6 =

5. 15 – 4 =

6. 10 – ____ = 9

7. 6 x 5 =

8. Double 7 =

9. 10 x 8 =

10. 45 ÷ 5 =

11. Half of 22 =

12. 50 ÷ 10 =

13. Count down in ones: 74, 73, 72, 71…
    What number comes next?

14. Count in threes: 21, 24, 27, 30…
    What number comes next?

15. What fraction is shaded?

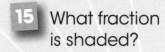

16. What time does the clock show?

17. How much money altogether?

18. What do the cherries weigh?

19. How much liquid in the jug?

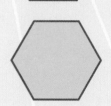

20. What shape is this?

Brodie's Brain Booster

I have a 20p coin. How many 5p coins could I swap it for?

12

Score:

1 Add 6 to 9.

2 4 + 8 =

3 15 + 7 =

4 17 subtract 8 =

5 16 – 9 =

6 10 –   = 10

7 9 x 5 =

8 Double 9 =

9 10 x 3 =

10 50 ÷ 5 =

11 Half of 24 =

12 70 ÷ 10 =

13 Count down in ones: 62, 61, 60, 59…
What number comes next?

14 Count in threes: 12, 15, 18, 21…
What number comes next?

15 What fraction is shaded?

16 What time does the clock show?

17 How much money altogether?

18 What does the melon weigh?

19 How much liquid in the jug?

20 What shape is this?

Addition

1 Add 4 to 8.

2 7 + 9 =

3 19 + 8 =

Subtraction

4 15 subtract 9 =

5 20 – 4 =

6 10 – ⬚ = 1

Multiplication

7 8 x 5 =

8 Double 11 =

9 10 x 10 =

Division

10 60 ÷ 5 =

11 Half of 26 =

12 80 ÷ 10 =

Number and place value

13 Count down in ones: 93, 92, 91, 90…
What number comes next?

14 Count in threes: 21, 24, 27, 30…
What number comes next?

Fractions

15 What fraction is shaded?

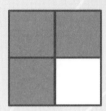

Measures

16 What time does the clock show?

17 How much money altogether?

16 What do the satsumas weigh?

19 How much liquid in the jug?

Geometry

20 What shape is this?

Score chart

Test	6	7	8	9	10	Progress
Score						

Score:

1 9 plus 7.

2 12 + 7 =

3 20p + 5p =

4 13 take away 4 =

5 18 – 3 =

6 11 – ___ = 5

7 Multiply 5 by 3.

8 2 x 8 =

9 10 x 4 =

10 25 ÷ 5 =

11 Share 16 between 2.

12 90 ÷ 10 =

13 Count in fives: 0, 5, 10, 15…
What number comes next?

14 What number does the tally show?

15 What fraction of the set of circles is shaded?

16 What time does the clock show?

17 How much money altogether?

18 The potatoes weigh $3\frac{1}{2}$kg. Draw the pointer at the correct place.

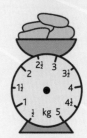

19 How much liquid in the cylinder?

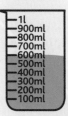

20 What shape is this?

Brodie's Brain Booster

I have a 20p coin. How many 2p coins could I swap it for?

TEST 12

1 8 plus 6.

2 11 + 7 =

3 18p + 6p =

4 19 take away 4.

5 19 − 7 =

6 12 − [   ] = 5

7 Multiply 5 by 4.

8 2 x 5 =

9 10 x 5 =

10 35 ÷ 5 =

11 Share 10 between 2.

12 20 ÷ 10 =

13 Count in fives: 10, 15, 20, 25…
What number comes next?

14 What number does the tally show?

15 What fraction
of the set of squares
is shaded?

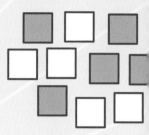

16 What time
does the
clock show?

17 How much money
altogether?

18 The carrots
weigh 2kg.
Draw the pointer
at the correct
place.

19 How much liquid
in the cylinder?

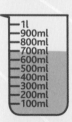

20 What shape is this?

Digit says...

Did you know that
there are 1000 grams in
a kilogram? That's a lot
of grams!

1   12 plus 4 =

2   13 + 7 =

3   19p + 4p =

4   18 take away 4 =

5   17 – 6 =

6   13 – _____ = 5

7   Multiply 5 by 5.

8   2 x 9 =

9   10 x 9 =

10   40 ÷ 5 =

11   Share 12 between 2.

12   10 ÷ 10 =

13   Count in fives: 15, 20, 25, 30...
What number comes next?

14   What number does the tally show?

15   What fraction of the set of rectangles is shaded?

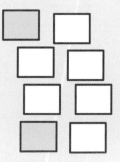

16   What time does the clock show?

17   How much money altogether?

18   The parsnips weigh 3kg. Draw the pointer at the correct place.

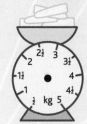

19   How much liquid in the cylinder?

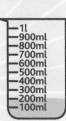

20   What shape is this?

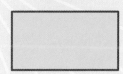

Brodie's Brain Booster

I have a 50p coin. How many 10p coins could I swap it for?

17

1 6 plus 7.

2 14 + 7 =

3 17p + 6p =

4 17 take away 4 =

5 17 – 8 =

6 14 –   = 5

7 Multiply 5 by 6.

8 2 x 7 =

9 10 x 8 =

10 45 ÷ 5 =

11 Share 14 between 2.

12 30 ÷ 10 =

13 Count in fives: 25, 30, 35, 40…
What number comes next?

14 What number does the tally show?

15 What fraction
of the set of squares
is shaded?

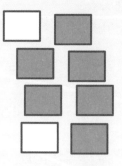

16 What time
does the
clock show?

17 How much money
altogether?

18 The onions
weigh 1kg.
Draw the pointer
at the correct
place.

19 How much liquid
in the cylinder?

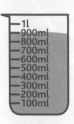

20 What shape is this?

Digit says...

Remember that a
pentagon has 5 sides
but I have only two –
top and bottom!

TEST 15

Brodie's Brain Booster

I have 50p. My sister has 35p. How much more than my sister have I got?

1 8 plus 8 =

2 15 + 7 =

3 18p + 9p =

4 16 take away 4 =

5 19 – 9 =

6 15 – ⬚ = 5

7 Multiply 5 by 7.

8 2 x 6 =

9 10 x 7 =

10 50 ÷ 5 =

11 Share 18 between 2.

12 40 ÷ 10 =

13 Count in fives: 35, 40, 45, 50…
What number comes next?

14 What number does the tally show?

‖‖‖‖ ‖‖‖‖

15 What fraction of the set of circles is shaded?

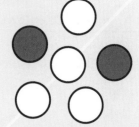

16 What time does the clock show?

17 How much money altogether?

18 The potatoes weigh 1½kg. Draw the pointer at the correct place.

19 How much liquid in the cylinder?

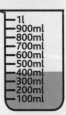

20 What shape is this?

Addition

1   5 plus 6 =

2   16 + 7 =

3   16p + 8p =

Subtraction

4   15 take away 4 =

5   15 – 15 =

6   16 – [ ] = 7

Multiplication

7   Multiply 5 by 8.

8   2 x 12 =

9   10 x 6 =

Division

10   55 ÷ 5 =

11   Share 20 between 2.

12   50 ÷ 10 =

Number and place value

13   Count in fives: 40, 45, 50, 55…
What number comes next?

14   What number does the tally show?

卌 卌丨

Fractions

15   What fraction of the set of triangles is shaded?

Measures

16   What time does the clock show?

17   How much money altogether?

16   The carrots weigh $2\frac{1}{2}$ kg. Draw the pointer at the correct place.

19   How much liquid in the cylinder?

Geometry

20   What shape is this?

Score chart

Test	11	12	13	14	15	Progress
Score						

Score:

1 What is the total of 8 and 5?

2 8 + 7 =

3 12 + 8 =

4 20 minus 4 =

5 13 – 4 =

6 20 – ____ = 5

7 2 multiplied by 8 =

8 9 x 5 =

9 7 x 10 =

10 Divide 45 by 5.

11 18 ÷ 2 =

12 60 ÷ 10 =

13 Count in tens: 0, 10, 20, 30…
What number comes next?

14 Write these numbers in order,
smallest first: 48 17 32

15 Colour half of
the circles.

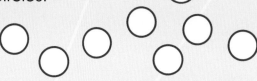

16 What time
does the
clock show?

17 How much money
altogether?

18 The parsnips
weigh 4kg.
Draw the pointer
at the correct
place.

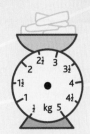

19 How much liquid
in the cylinder?

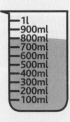

20 How many sides does
a square have?

Digit says...

Did you know
that a hexagon
has 6 sides?

Score:

1 What is the total of 3 and 6?

2 6 + 7 =

3 13 + 8 =

4 20 minus 8 =

5 13 – 7 =

6 20 – ___ = 2

7 2 multiplied by 4 =

8 3 x 5 =

9 9 x 10 =

10 Divide 50 by 5.

11 16 ÷ 2 =

12 100 ÷ 10 =

13 Count in tens: 40, 50, 60, 70…
What number comes next?

14 Write these numbers in order,
smallest first: 39 62 17

15 Colour half of the stars.

16 What time
does the
clock show?

17 How much money
altogether?

18 The onions
weigh 5kg.
Draw the pointer
at the correct
place.

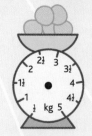

19 How much liquid
in the cylinder?

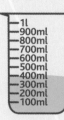

20 How many sides does
a triangle have?

Brodie's Brain Booster

I have 50p. My sister has 35p.
How much have we got altogether?

Score:

1 What is the total of 7 and 8?

2 9 + 4 =

3 14 + 7 =

4 20 minus 5 =

5 13 – 8 =

6 20 – ___ = 4

7 2 multiplied by 5 =

8 4 x 5 =

9 8 x 10 =

10 Divide 20 by 5.

11 14 ÷ 2 =

12 40 ÷ 10 =

13 Count in tens: 50, 60, 70, 80…
What number comes next?

14 Write these numbers in order,
smallest first: 95 73 37

15 Colour half of the triangles.

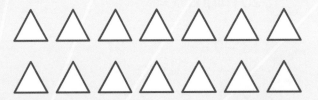

16 What time
does the
clock show?

17 How much money
altogether?

18 The potatoes
weigh 2½kg.
Draw the pointer
at the correct
place.

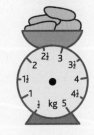

19 How much liquid
in the cylinder?

20 How many sides does
a rectangle have?

TEST 19

Score:

Brodie's Brain Booster

I have 50p. How much more money do I need so that I have £1?

1 What is the total of 9 and 5?

2 8 + 9 =

3 15 + 6 =

4 20 minus 6 =

5 13 – 9 =

6 20 – ⬚ = 9

7 2 multiplied by 6 =

8 6 x 5 =

9 6 x 10 =

10 Divide 30 by 5.

11 12 ÷ 2 =

12 50 ÷ 10 =

13 Count in tens: 20, 30, 40, 50…
What number comes next?

14 Write these numbers in order, smallest first: 94 72 58

15 Colour half of the squares.

16 What time does the clock show?

17 How much money altogether?

18 The carrots weigh $4\frac{1}{2}$kg. Draw the pointer at the correct place.

19 How much liquid in the cylinder?

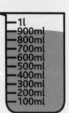

20 How many sides does a hexagon have?

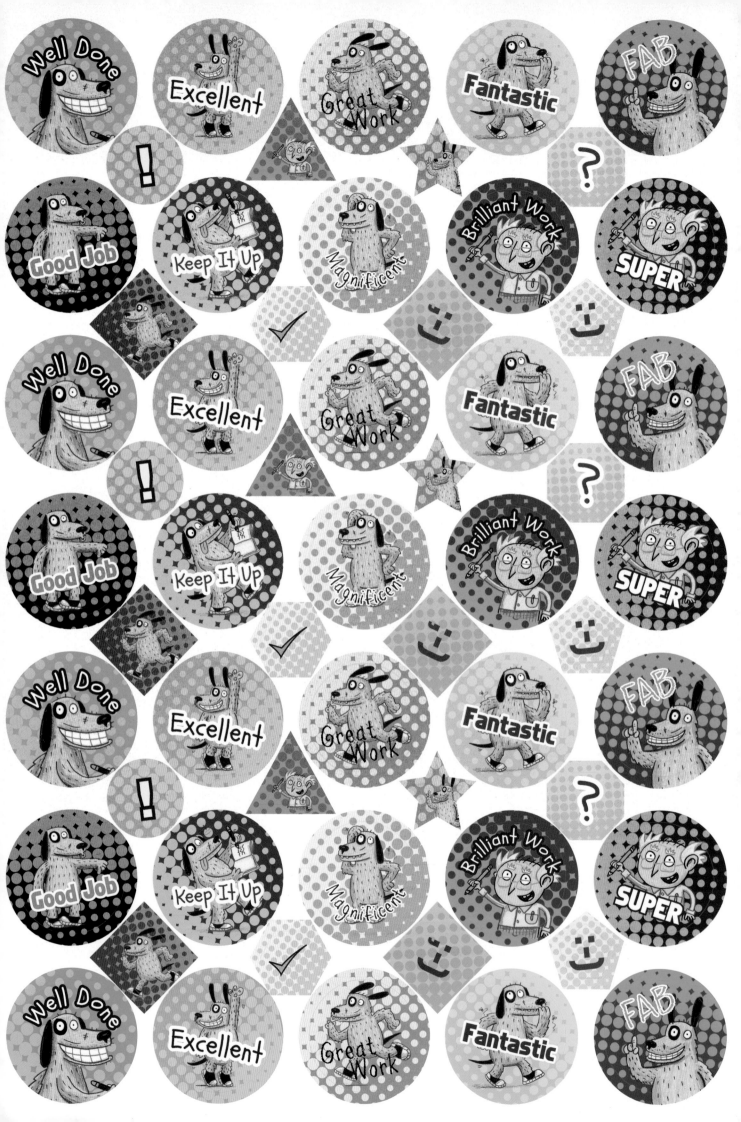

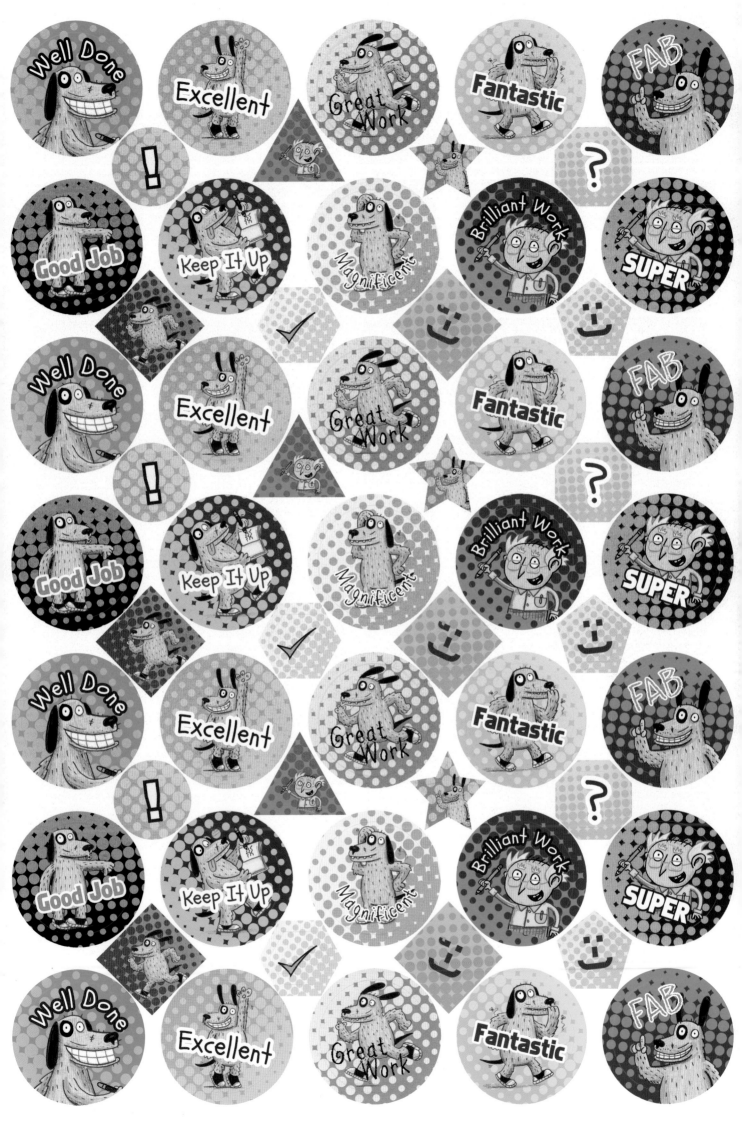

Score:

1 What is the total of 6 and 5?

2 7 + 6 =

3 17 + 8 =

4 20 minus 9 =

5 13 – 5 =

6 20 – ____ = 7

7 2 multiplied by 7 =

8 7 x 5 =

9 4 x 10 =

10 Divide 40 by 5.

11 20 ÷ 2 =

12 80 ÷ 10 =

13 Count in tens: 50, 60, 70, 80…
What number comes next?

14 Write these numbers in order,
smallest first: 24, 81, 68

15 Colour half of the rectangles.

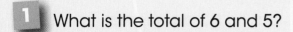

16 What time
does the
clock show?

17 How much money
altogether?

18 The parsnips
weigh 1½kg.
Draw the pointer
at the correct
place.

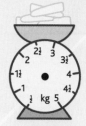

19 How much liquid
in the cylinder?

20 How many sides does
a pentagon have?

Digit says...

Remember that
an octagon has 8
sides.

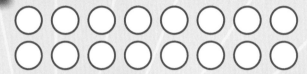

Addition

1 What is the total of 7 and 9?

2 $2 + 9 =$

3 $17 + 6 =$

Subtraction

4 20 minus 3 =

5 $13 - 6 =$

6 $20 - \boxed{} = 6$

Multiplication

7 2 multiplied by 9 =

8 $8 \times 5 =$

9 $5 \times 10 =$

Division

10 Divide 35 by 5.

11 $24 \div 2 =$

12 $90 \div 10 =$

Number and place value

13 Count in tens: 60, 70, 80, 90…
What number comes next?

14 Write these numbers in order,
smallest first: 34 27 41

Fractions

15 Colour half of the circles.

Measures

16 What time does
the clock show?

17 How much money
altogether?

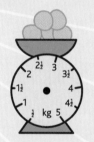

16 The onions
weigh $3\frac{1}{2}$kg.
Draw the pointer
at the correct
place.

19 How much liquid
in the cylinder?

Geometry

20 How many sides does
a hexagon have?

Score chart

Test	16	17	18	19	20	Progress
Score						

26

1 Add 20 to 40.

2 43 + 8 =

3 32 + 20 =

4 Subtract 40 from 70.

5 42 – 6 =

6 79 – 20 =

7 5 multiplied by 8 =

8 7 x 2 =

9 10 x 2 =

10 Divide 30 by 5.

11 24 ÷ 2 =

12 70 divided by 10 =

13 Count down in twos: 22, 20, 18, 16…
What number comes next?

14 Write these numbers in order,
smallest first: 163 98 211

15 Colour one quarter of the circles.

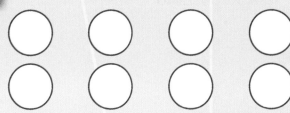

16 Draw hands
on the clock
face to show
the time 5 o'clock.

17 How much
more money
do I need
to make 30p?

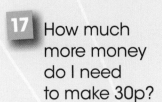

18 How much less than 1kg is 200g?

19 Mark the
level of liquid
at 400ml.

```
1l
900ml
800ml
700ml
600ml
500ml
400ml
300ml
200ml
100ml
```

20 How many sides
does a square have?

Brodie's Brain Booster

My sister has 35p.
How much more
money does she need so
that she has £1?

27

TEST 22

1 Add 30 to 40.

2 53 + 8 =

3 47 + 20 =

4 Subtract 40 from 90.

5 53 – 6 =

6 81 – 20 =

7 5 multiplied by 7 =

8 4 x 2 =

9 10 x 3 =

10 Divide 15 by 5.

11 22 ÷ 2 =

12 30 divided by 10 =

13 Count down in twos: 30, 28, 26, 24…
What number comes next?

14 Write these numbers in order,
smallest first: 121 211 12

15 Colour one quarter of the stars.

16 Draw hands
on the clock
face to show
the time 9 o'clock.

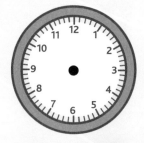

17 How much
more money
do I need
to make 30p?

18 How much less than 1kg is 400g?

19 Mark the
level of liquid
at 700ml.

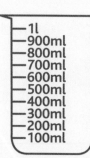

20 How many sides
does a triangle have?

Digit says...

Did you know that five 20p
coins are worth £1?

Brodie's Brain Booster

Brodie's Brain Booster

There are 24 hours in a day. How many hours are there altogether in 2 days?

1 Add 50 to 40. [ ]

2 33 + 8 = [ ]

3 18 + 20 = [ ]

4 Subtract 30 from 70. [ ]

5 64 – 6 = [ ]

6 47 – 20 = [ ]

7 5 multiplied by 6 = [ ]

8 5 x 2 = [ ]

9 10 x 4 = [ ]

10 Divide 20 by 5. [ ]

11 20 ÷ 2 = [ ]

12 40 divided by 10 = [ ]

13 Count down in twos: 24, 22, 20, 18…
What number comes next?

[ ]

14 Write these numbers in order,
smallest first: 473 734 74

[ ]

15 Colour one quarter of the triangles.

△ △ △ △ △ △
△ △ △ △ △ △
△ △ △ △

16 Draw hands on the clock face to show the time 5 o'clock.

17 How much more money do I need to make 30p?

[ ]

18 How much less than 1kg is 900g?

19 Mark the level of liquid at 300ml.

20 How many sides does a rectangle have?

[ ]

Score:

1 Add 10 to 40.

2 63 + 8 =

3 51 + 20 =

4 Subtract 50 from 80.

5 31 – 6 =

6 65 – 20 =

7 5 multiplied by 5 =

8 6 x 2 =

9 10 x 5 =

10 Divide 25 by 5.

11 18 ÷ 2 =

12 50 divided by 10 =

13 Count down in twos: 26, 24, 22, 20…
What number comes next?

14 Write these numbers in order,
smallest first: 892 98 928

15 Colour one quarter of the squares.

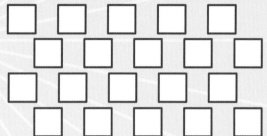

16 Draw hands
on the clock
face to show
the time 12 o'clock.

17 How much
more money
do I need
to make 30p?

18 How much less than 1kg is 700g?

19 Mark the
level of liquid
at 800ml.

```
1l
900ml
800ml
700ml
600ml
500ml
400ml
300ml
200ml
100ml
```

20 How many sides
does an octagon have?

Digit says...

I can count in threes all the
way to 30. I think of dog
biscuits and count like this:
3, 6, 9, 12, 15, 18, 21, 24, 27, 30.

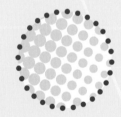

1 Add 60 to 30.

2 73 + 8 =

3 64 + 20 =

4 Subtract 20 from 70.

5 74 – 6 =

6 86 – 20 =

7 5 multiplied by 9 =

8 8 x 2 =

9 10 x 6 =

10 Divide 35 by 5.

11 16 ÷ 2 =

12 60 divided by 10 =

13 Count down in twos: 28, 26, 24, 22…
What number comes next?

14 Write these numbers in order,
smallest first: 245 542 452

15 Colour one quarter of the rectangles.

16 Draw hands on the clock face to show the time 4 o'clock.

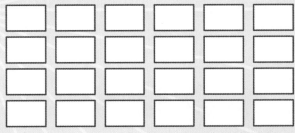

17 How much more money do I need to make 30p?

18 How much less than 1kg is 100g?

19 Mark the level of liquid at 200ml.

```
1l
900ml
800ml
700ml
600ml
500ml
400ml
300ml
200ml
100ml
```

20 How many sides does a pentagon have?

Addition

1 Add 40 to 30.

2 83 + 8 =

3 73 + 20 =

Subtraction

4 Subtract 20 from 80.

5 85 – 6 =

6 99 – 20

Multiplication

7 5 multiplied by 11 =

8 9 x 2 =

9 10 x 7 =

Division

10 Divide 40 by 5.

11 14 ÷ 2 =

12 80 divided by 10 =

Number and place value

13 Count down in twos: 20, 18, 16, 14…
What number comes next?

14 Write these numbers in order,
smallest first: 316 163 613

Fractions

15 Colour one quarter of the circles.

Measures

16 Draw hands
on the clock
face to show
the time 6 o'clock.

17 How much
more money
do I need
to make 30p?

16 How much less than 1kg is 600g?

19 Mark the
level of liquid
at 100ml.

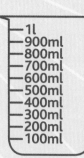

Geometry

20 How many sides does
an octagon have?

Score chart

Test	21	22	23	24	25	Progress
Score						

1 60 plus 30 =

2 6 + 7 + 8 =

3 56 + 20 =

4 90 minus 50 =

5 71 – 6 =

6 I have 20p. I spend 14p. What change do I get?

7 10 multiplied by 3 =

8 2 x 6 =

9 7 x 5 =

10 Divide 22 by 2.

11 10 ÷ 5 =

12 250 ÷ 10 =

13 Count down in fives: 50, 45, 40, 35… What number comes next?

14 Write < or >. 7   9

15 Colour three quarters of the circles.

16 Draw hands on the clock face to show a half past 11.

17 How much more money do I need to make 50p?

18 How much less than 1kg is 800g?

19 Mark the level of liquid at 600ml.

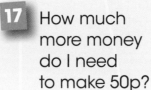

20 How many vertices does a square have?

Digit says...

I can count back in fives from 50 all the way to 0. This is how I do it: 50, 45, 40, 35, 30, 25, 20, 15, 10, 5, 0.

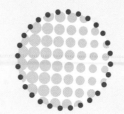

Score:

What number is double 16?

1 40 plus 30 =

2 5 + 7 + 9 =

3 17 + 30 =

4 90 minus 40 =

5 31 – 6 =

6 I have 20p. I spend 12p. What is my change?

7 10 multiplied by 4 =

8 2 x 7 =

9 4 x 5 =

10 Divide 14 by 2.

11 15 ÷ 5 =

12 140 ÷ 10 =

13 Count down in fives: 55, 50, 45, 40… What number comes next?

14 Write < or >. 12 _____ 9

15 Colour three quarters of the stars.

16 Draw hands on the clock face to show a half past 7.

17 How much more money do I need to make 50p?

18 How much less than 1kg is 100g?

19 Mark the level of liquid at 700ml.

20 How many vertices does a triangle have?

Score:

1 50 plus 30 =

2 8 + 3 + 1 =

3 19 + 20 =

4 90 minus 60 =

5 41 – 6 =

6 I have 20p. I spend 17p. What change do I get?

7 10 multiplied by 5 =

8 2 x 8 =

9 5 x 5 =

10 Divide 16 by 2.

11 20 ÷ 5 =

12 170 ÷ 10 =

13 Count down in fives: 35, 30, 25, 20… What number comes next?

14 Write < or >. 3 _____ 4.

15 Colour three quarters of the triangles.

16 Draw hands on the clock face to show a half past 8.

17 How much more money do I need to make 50p?

18 How much less than 1kg is 200g?

19 Mark the level of liquid at 400ml.

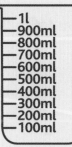

20 How many vertices does a rectangle have?

Digit says...

Remember that there are 60 minutes in 1 hour and just 1 hour before my dinner time!

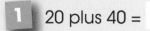

1   20 plus 40 =

2   9 + 5 + 3 =

3   27 + 40 =

4   90 minus 30 =

5   51 – 6 =

6   I have 20p. I spend 8p. What is my change?

7   10 multiplied by 6 =

8   2 x 9 =

9   6 x 5 =

10   Divide 18 by 2.

11   30 ÷ 5 =

12   360 ÷ 10 =

13   Count down in fives: 40, 35, 30, 25… What number comes next?

14   Write < or >. 7 ____ 5

15   Colour three quarters of the squares.

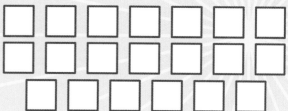

16   Draw hands on the clock face to show a half past 4.

17   How much more money do I need to make 50p?

18   How much less than 1kg is 500g?

19   Mark the level of liquid at 200ml.

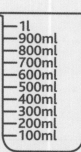

20   How many vertices does a octagon have?

Brodie's Brain Booster

Which month comes before January?

36

TEST 30

Score: ___

1 40 plus 40 = ___

2 6 + 6 + 7 = ___

3 34 + 50 = ___

4 90 minus 20 = ___

5 61 – 6 = ___

6 I have 20p. I spend 13p. What is my change?

___

7 10 multiplied by 7 = ___

8 2 x 10 = ___

9 8 x 5 = ___

10 Divide 20 by 2.

11 35 ÷ 5 = ___

12 420 ÷ 10 = ___

13 Count down in fives: 30, 25, 20, 15…
What number comes next?

___

14 Write < or >. 6 ___ 9

15 Colour three quarters of the circles.

16 Draw hands on the clock face to show a half past 1.

17 How much more money do I need to make 50p?

___

18 How much less than 1kg is 400g?

___

19 Mark the level of liquid at 900ml.

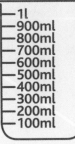

20 How many vertices does a pentagon have?

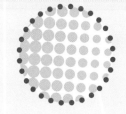

37

Addition

1 50 plus 50 =

2 8 + 4 + 5 =

3 47 + 20 =

Subtraction

4 90 minus 70 =

5 81 – 6 =

6 I have 20p. I spend 9p.
What is my change?

Multiplication

7 10 multiplied by 8 =

8 2 x 11 =

9 9 x 5 =

Division

10 Divide 24 by 2.

11 40 ÷ 5 =

12 710 ÷ 10 =

Number and place value

13 Count down in fives: 20, 15, 10, 5…
What number comes next?

14 Write < or >. 7   5

Fractions

15 Colour three quarters of the circles.

○ ○ ○ ○ ○ ○ ○ ○ ○
○ ○ ○ ○ ○ ○ ○ ○ ○

Measures

16 Draw hands on the clock face to show a half past 3.

17 How much more money do I need to make 50p?

16 How much less than 1kg is 700g?

19 Mark the level of liquid at 800ml.

Geometry

20 How many vertices does an octagon have?

Score chart

Test	26	27	28	29	30	Progress
Score						

Score:

1 40 plus 20 =

2 19 + 6 + 3 =

3 4 + _____ = 9

4 100 take away 50 =

5 58 − 16 =

6 I have 50p. I spend 28p. What is my change?

7 2 multiplied by 9 =

8 7 x 5 =

9 10 x 12 =

10 Divide 300 by 10.

11 45 ÷ 9 =

12 16 divided by 2 =

13 Write < or >. 26 _____ 18

14 What number does the tally show?

|||| |||| |||| ||

15 Colour one third of the circles.

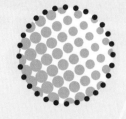

16 Draw hands on the clock face to show a quarter past 4.

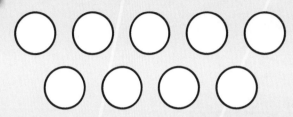

17 How much more money do I need to make £1?

18 How much less than 1kg is 250g?

19 Mark the level of liquid at 450ml.

1l
900ml
800ml
700ml
600ml
500ml
400ml
300ml
200ml
100ml

20 How many vertices does a square have?

Brodie's Brain Booster

How many centimetres make half a metre?

TEST 32

1 30 plus 20 =

2 17 + 7 + 2 =

3 5 + ___ = 14

4 100 take away 20 =

5 47 –15 =

6 I have 50p. I spend 16p. What is my change?

7 2 multiplied by 4 =

8 9 x 5 =

9 10 x 20 =

10 Divide 800 by 10.

11 35 ÷ 7 =

12 18 divided by 2 =

13 Write < or >. 15 ___ 18

14 What number does the tally show?

卌 卌 IIII

15 Colour one third of the stars.

16 Draw hands on the clock face to show a quarter past 1.

17 How much more money do I need to make £1?

18 How much less than 1kg is 950g?

19 Mark the level of liquid at 250ml.

—1l
—900ml
—800ml
—700ml
—600ml
—500ml
—400ml
—300ml
—200ml
—100ml

20 How many vertices does a triangle have?

Digit says...

Did you know that there are 15 minutes in a quarter of an hour?

Score:

1 50 plus 20 =

2 16 + 7 + 4 =

3 6 + _____ = 19

4 100 take away 40 =

5 69 – 13 =

6 I have 50p. I spend 28p. What is my change?

7 2 multiplied by 8 =

8 3 x 5 =

9 10 x 30 =

10 Divide 600 by 10.

11 55 ÷ 11 =

12 20 divided by 2 =

13 Write < or >. 32 _____ 19

14 What number does the tally show?

|||| |||| |||| ||||

15 Colour one third of the triangles.

16 Draw hands on the clock face to show a quarter past 9.

17 How much more money do I need to make £1?

18 How much less than 1kg is 350g?

19 Mark the level of liquid at 750ml.

```
1l
900ml
800ml
700ml
600ml
500ml
400ml
300ml
200ml
100ml
```

20 How many vertices does a rectangle have?

Brodie's Brain Booster

How many grams are there in half a kilogram?

TEST 34 Score:

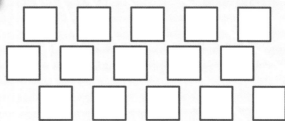

Digit says...

I can count back in threes from 30 all the way to 0. This is how I do it: 30, 27, 24, 21, 18, 15, 12, 9, 6, 3, 0.

1 70 plus 20 =

2 15 + 6 + 2 =

3 7 + ____ = 12

4 100 take away 70 =

5 77 – 11 =

6 I have 50p. I spend 42p. What is my change?

7 2 multiplied by 6 =

8 5 x 5 =

9 10 x 40 =

10 Divide 900 by 10.

11 25 ÷ 5 =

12 22 divided by 2 =

13 Write < or >. 45 ____ 54

14 What number does the tally show?

卌 卌 卌 卌 |||

15 Colour one third of the squares.

16 Draw hands on the clock face to show a quarter past 2.

17 How much more money do I need to make £1?

18 How much less than 1kg is 450g?

19 Mark the level of liquid at 950ml.

- 1l
- 900ml
- 800ml
- 700ml
- 600ml
- 500ml
- 400ml
- 300ml
- 200ml
- 100ml

20 How many vertices does an octagon have?

Score:

1 80 plus 20 =

2 18 + 6 + 4 =

3 6 + _____ = 10

4 100 take away 60 =

5 89 – 16 =

6 I have 50p. I spend 35p. What is my change?

7 2 multiplied by 10 =

8 11 x 5 =

9 10 x 50 =

10 Divide 400 by 10.

11 60 ÷ 12 =

12 24 divided by 2 =

13 Write < or >. 73 _____ 37

14 What number does the tally show?

|||| |||| |||| ||||

15 Colour one third of the rectangles.

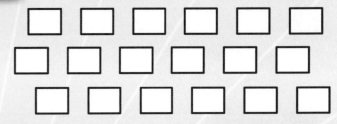

16 Draw hands on the clock face to show a quarter past 7.

17 How much more money do I need to make £1?

18 How much less than 1kg is 550g?

19 Mark the level of liquid at 650ml.

```
— 1l
—900ml
—800ml
—700ml
—600ml
—500ml
—400ml
—300ml
—200ml
—100ml
```

20 How many vertices does a pentagon have?

Brodie's Brain Booster

What time is it exactly 1 hour after 11.30am?

1 60 plus 20 =

2 15 + 9 + 3 =

3 8 + _____ = 12

Subtraction

4 100 take away 80 =

5 75 − 12 =

6 I have 50p. I spend 41p.
What is my change?

Multiplication

7 2 multiplied by 12 =

8 8 x 5 =

9 10 x 6 =

Division

10 Divide 500 by 10.

11 40 ÷ 8 =

12 26 ÷ 2 =

Number and place value

13 Write < or >: 26 _____ 62

14 What number does the tally show?

𝍷𝍷𝍷𝍷𝍷 𝍷𝍷𝍷𝍷𝍷 𝍷𝍷𝍷𝍷𝍷 𝍷𝍷𝍷𝍷𝍷 𝍷𝍷

Fractions

15 Colour one third of the circles.

Measures

16 Draw hands on the clock face to show quarter past 3.

17 How much more money do I need to make £1?

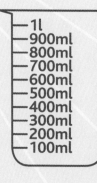

16 How much less than 1kg is 650g?

19 Mark the level of liquid at 350ml.

> — 1l
> — 900ml
> — 800ml
> — 700ml
> — 600ml
> — 500ml
> — 400ml
> — 300ml
> — 200ml
> — 100ml

Geometry

20 How many vertices does an octagon have?

Score chart

Test	31	32	33	34	35	Progress
Score						

ANSWERS

	Test 1	Test 2	Test 3	Test 4	Test 5	Progress Test 1
1	17	13	14	13	11	15
2	13	14	14	11	13	16
3	20	20	19	21	23	24
4	4	5	7	8	5	6
5	4	4	6	5	6	4
6	6	5	8	8	6	8
7	30	15	45	50	0	35
8	18	14	4	6	24	0
9	70	60	80	10	30	90
10	6	8	9	5	4	7
11	8	9	11	5	6	7
12	8	9	4	3	5	6
13	72	89	60	46	83	79
14	8	22	32	36	24	42
15	$\frac{1}{2}$	$\frac{1}{4}$	$\frac{1}{3}$	$\frac{1}{2}$	$\frac{1}{4}$	$\frac{3}{4}$
16	6 o'clock	8 o'clock	4 o'clock	1 o'clock	9 o'clock	11 o'clock
17	22p	16p	12p	25p	17p	15p
18	2kg	$2\frac{1}{2}$ kg	3kg	$4\frac{1}{2}$ kg	5kg	$1\frac{1}{2}$ kg
19	2l	$\frac{1}{2}$ l	$2\frac{1}{2}$ l	3l	$1\frac{1}{2}$ l	$2\frac{1}{2}$ l
20	triangle	square	rectangle	hexagaon	octagon	pentagon

	Test 6	Test 7	Test 8	Test 9	Test 10	Progress Test 2
1	13	14	12	13	15	12
2	14	16	14	13	12	16
3	20	21	25	27	22	27
4	5	8	5	7	9	6
5	8	8	11	11	7	16
6	4	6	2	1	0	9
7	35	15	20	30	45	40
8	8	16	12	14	18	22
9	60	90	20	80	30	100
10	8	11	3	9	10	12
11	9	10	8	11	12	13
12	10	6	4	5	7	8
13	54	77	81	70	58	89
14	12	15	27	33	24	33
15	$\frac{1}{2}$	$\frac{1}{4}$	$\frac{1}{3}$	$\frac{1}{2}$	$\frac{1}{4}$	$\frac{3}{4}$
16	half past 6	half past 9	half past 2	half past 4	half past 1	half past 12
17	22p	25p	21p	30p	23p	27p
18	2kg	5kg	$1\frac{1}{2}$ kg	$2\frac{1}{2}$ kg	4kg	$4\frac{1}{2}$ kg
19	$1\frac{1}{2}$ l	3l	$\frac{1}{2}$ l	$1\frac{1}{2}$ l	$2\frac{1}{2}$ l	1l
20	triangle	square	rectangle	hexagon	octagon	pentagon

	Test 11	Test 12	Test 13	Test 14	Test 15	Progress Test 3
1	16	14	16	13	16	11
2	19	18	20	21	22	23
3	25p	24p	23p	23p	27p	24p
4	9	15	14	13	12	11
5	15	12	11	9	10	0
6	6	7	8	9	10	9
7	15	20	25	30	35	40
8	16	10	18	14	12	24
9	40	50	90	80	70	60
10	5	7	8	9	10	11
11	8	5	6	7	9	10
12	9	2	1	3	4	5
13	20	30	35	45	55	60
14	7	6	8	9	10	11
15	$\frac{1}{2}$ or $\frac{3}{6}$	$\frac{5}{10}$ or $\frac{1}{2}$	$\frac{2}{8}$ or $\frac{1}{4}$	$\frac{6}{8}$ or $\frac{3}{4}$	$\frac{2}{6}$ or $\frac{1}{3}$	$\frac{2}{8}$ or $\frac{1}{4}$
16	quarter past 6	quarter past 11	quarter past 1	quarter past 4	quarter past 3	quarter past 10
17	32p	35p	31p	40p	50p	35p
18						
19	600ml	700ml	200ml	900ml	400ml	500ml
20	triangle	square	rectangle	hexagon	octagon	pentagon

	Test 16	Test 17	Test 18	Test 19	Test 20	Progress Test 4
1	13	9	15	14	11	16
2	15	13	13	17	13	11
3	20	21	21	21	25	23
4	16	12	15	14	11	17
5	9	6	5	4	8	7
6	15	18	16	11	13	14
7	16	8	10	12	14	18
8	45	15	20	30	35	40
9	70	90	80	60	40	50
10	9	10	4	6	8	7
11	9	8	7	6	10	12
12	6	10	4	5	8	9
13	40	80	90	60	90	100
14	17 32 48	17 39 62	37 73 95	58 72 94	24 68 81	27 34 41
15	4 coloured	6 coloured	7 coloured	10 coloured	12 coloured	8 coloured
16	quarter to 5	quarter to 1	quarter to 7	quarter to 11	quarter to 2	quarter to 12
17	62p	57p	61p	56p	53p	75p
18						
19	800ml	400ml	300ml	900ml	1l	700ml
20	4	3	4	6	5	6

	Test 21	Test 22	Test 23	Test 24	Test 25	Progress Test 5
1	60	70	90	50	90	70
2	51	61	41	71	81	91
3	52	67	38	71	84	93
4	30	50	40	30	50	60
5	36	47	58	25	68	79
6	59	61	27	45	66	79
7	40	35	30	25	45	55
8	14	8	10	12	16	18
9	20	30	40	50	60	70
10	6	3	4	5	7	8
11	12	11	10	9	8	7
12	7	3	4	5	6	8
13	14	22	16	18	20	12
14	98 163 211	12 121 211	74 473 734	98 892 928	245 452 542	163 316 613
15	2 coloured	3 coloured	4 coloured	5 coloured	6 coloured	5 coloured
16						
17	8p	5p	9p	13p	14p	10p
18	800g	600g	100g	300g	900g	400g
19						
20	4	3	4	8	5	8

	Test 26	Test 27	Test 28	Test 29	Test 30	Progress Test 6
1	90	70	80	60	80	100
2	21	21	12	17	19	17
3	76	47	39	67	84	67
4	40	50	30	60	70	20
5	65	25	35	45	55	75
6	6p	8p	3p	12p	7p	11p
7	30	40	50	60	70	80
8	12	14	16	18	20	22
9	35	20	25	30	40	45
10	11	7	8	9	10	12
11	2	3	4	6	7	8
12	25	14	17	36	42	71
13	30	35	15	20	10	0
14	<	>	<	>	<	>
15	6 coloured	9 coloured	12 coloured	15 coloured	18 coloured	15 coloured
16						
17	5p	8p	9p	18p	19p	15p
18	200g	900g	800g	500g	600g	300g
19						
20	4	3	4	8	5	8

	Test 31	Test 32	Test 33	Test 34	Test 35	Progress Test 7
1	60	50	70	90	100	80
2	28	26	27	23	28	27
3	5	9	13	5	4	4
4	50	80	60	30	40	20
5	42	32	56	66	73	63
6	22p	34p	22p	8p	15p	9p
7	18	8	16	12	20	24
8	35	45	15	25	55	40
9	120	200	300	400	500	60
10	30	80	60	90	40	50
11	5	5	5	5	5	5
12	8	9	10	11	12	13
13	>	<	>	<	>	<
14	17	14	20	23	19	22
15	3 coloured	4 coloured	2 coloured	5 coloured	6 coloured	4 coloured
16						
17	60p	40p	20p	80p	80p	30p
18	750g	50g	650g	550g	450g	350g
19						
20	4	3	4	8	5	8

Brodie's Brain Booster

Test 1	14 days
Test 3	2
Test 5	5
Test 7	2
Test 9	4
Test 11	10
Test 13	5
Test 15	15p
Test 17	85p
Test 19	50p
Test 21	65p
Test 23	48
Test 25	15
Test 27	32
Test 29	December
Test 31	50
Test 33	500
Test 35	12.30pm

Digit says...

"Well done and see you next time"